Pop Hits for Professional Singers

Published by
Wise Publications
8/9 Frith Street, London W1D 3JB, England.

Exclusive Distributors:
Music Sales Limited
8/9 Frith Street, London W1D 3JB, England.
Music Sales Pty Limited
120 Rothschild Avenue, Rosebery, NSW 2018, Australia.

Order No. AM90077
ISBN 0-7119-3141-0

Compiled by Lucy Holliday.
Cover photographs courtesy of London Features International.
Printed in Malta by Interprint Limited.

Your Guarantee of Quality
As publishers, we strive to produce every book to the highest commercial standards.
This book has been carefully designed to minimise awkward page turns and to make playing from it a real pleasure.
Particular care has been given to specifying acid-free, neutral-sized paper made from pulps which have not been elemental chlorine bleached.
This pulp is from farmed sustainable forests and was produced with special regard for the environment.
Throughout, the printing and binding have been planned to ensure a sturdy, attractive publication which should give years of enjoyment.
If your copy fails to meet our high standards, please inform us and we will gladly replace it.

www.musicsales.com

CD TRACKS

Disc 1

1. All This Time (Hector / Mac / Tennant) Universal Music Publishing Limited/ Chrysalis Music Limited/Rokstone Music Limited.
2. Beautiful (Perry) Famous Music Publishing Limited.
3. Born To Try (Goodrem / Mtawarira) Sony/ATV Music Publishing (UK) Limited.
4. Complicated (Lavigne / Christy / Alspach / Edwards) Warner/Chappell North America Limited/Rondor Music (London) Limited.
5. Don't Know Why (Harris) Sony/ATV Music Publishing (UK) Limited.
6. For What It's Worth (Persson / Svensson) Universal Music Publishing Limited.
7. The Closest Thing To Crazy (Batt) Sony/ATV Music Publishing (UK) Limited.
8. Heaven (Adams / Vallance) Rondor Music (London) Limited.
9. Hopelessly Devoted To You (Farrar) Famous Music Publishing Limited.
10. How Come You Don't Call Me (Prince) Universal/MCA Music Limited.
11. I Wish I Knew How It Would Feel To Be Free (Taylor / Dallas) Westminster Music Limited.
12. I'm Gonna Getcha Good! (Twain / Lange) Universal Music Publishing Limited/ Out Of Pocket Productions Limited/Zomba Music Publishers Limited.
13. In These Shoes (Glenister / MacColl / Correa / Lastio) Warner/Chappell Music Limited/Chrysalis Music Limited/Copyright Control.

Disc 2

1. Ironic (Morissette / Ballard) Universal/MCA Music Limited.
2. Love At First Sight (Minogue / Stannard / Gallagher / Howes / Harrington) Universal Music Publishing Limited/Sony/ATV Music Publishing (UK) Limited/ EMI Music Publishing Limited/The International Music Network Limited.
3. Murder On The Dancefloor (Alexander / Ellis-Bextor) Warner/Chappell Music Limited/Rondor Music (London) Limited.
4. My Heart Will Go On (Love Theme From 'Titanic') (Jennings / Horner) International Music Publications Limited/Rondor Music (London) Limited.
5. Nothing Compares 2 U (Prince) Universal/MCA Music Limited.
6. Only Trust Your Heart (Cahn / Carter) Universal/MCA Music Limited.
7. Son Of A Preacher Man (Hurley / Wilkins) Sony/ATV Music Publishing (UK) Limited.
8. (Take A Little) Piece Of My Heart (Ragovoy / Berns) Sony/ATV Music Publishing (UK) Limited.
9. There Must Be An Angel (Playing With My Heart) (Lennox / Stewart) BMG Music Publishing Limited.
10. A Thousand Miles (Carlton) Universal Music Publishing Limited.
11. Time After Time (Lauper / Hyman) Warner/Chappell North America/ Sony/ATV Music Publishing (UK) Limited.
12. The Tide Is High (Get The Feeling) (Holt / Barrett / Evans / Padley / Godfrey) The Sparta Florida Music Group Limited/Universal Music Publishing Limited.
13. The Time Is Now (Brydon / Murphy) Chrysalis Music Limited.
14. Toxic (Dennis / Karlsson / Winnberg / Jonback) EMI Music Publishing Limited/Universal Music Publishing Limited.

CD backing vocals by Elly Barnes.

Wise Publications
London / New York / Paris / Sydney / Copenhagen / Berlin / Madrid / Tokyo

24-95

Disc 1

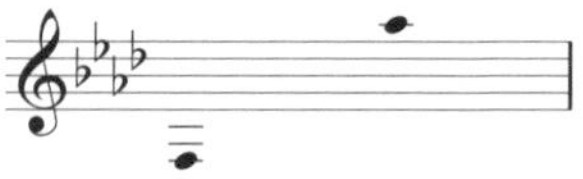

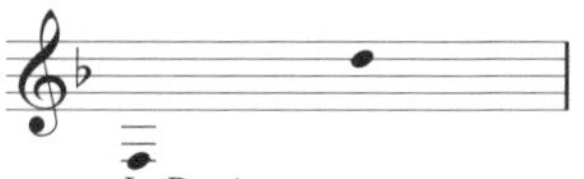

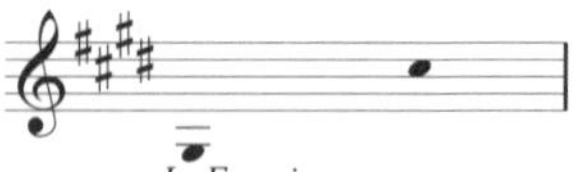

Disc 2

In G major
In E♭ minor
In E major
In E major
In F major
In E♭ major
In E major
In E♭ major
In C major
In B major
In C major
In C major
In A minor
In C minor

All This Time

Words & Music by Wayne Hector, Steve Mac & Lorne Tennant

F♯
Badd9
Stand - ing at the edge of my or - di - na - ry life.
And all these clouds of doubt have cleared a - round my mind.
F♯
Badd9
And now I'm look - ing far a - head, I on - ly see clear blue skies.
And now I'm look - ing far a - head, I'm look - ing with brand new eyes.
F♯
Badd9
F♯/A♯
6fr
I hope this feel - ing lasts me un - til the end of time.
Well I can't see the fu - ture but I know it's look - ing bright.
C♯
4fr
Badd9
Now I don't see the things that bring me down like I used to, no.
Nev - er thought we could sur - vive what we've come through, no.

C#
4fr
B
F#/C#
C#
4fr
Oh, there were times we felt like giv - ing up but we came through.
Oh, there were times we felt like giv - ing up but we had to.
All this
F#
C#
4fr
time. We've come a long, long way I've wait - ed a life -
Badd9
C#
4fr
F#/C#
C#
4fr
- time for to - day. I'm pray - ing this mo - ment's here to stay. All this
3
F#
C#
4fr
F#/C#
C#
4fr
time. When ev - 'ry - one else said I was wrong you gave me a rea -

Badd9
C♯
4fr
F♯/C♯
C♯
4fr
- son to be strong. You gave me the will to car - ry on. All this
1.
2.
F♯
G♯m7
4fr
time. 2. You kiss my mood a - way, time. It's like a sec - ond chance at
D♯m7
C♯/E♯
life, so ma - ny peo - ple pass it by. And you know it's a shame 'cause they
3
B
D♯m
G♯m7
4fr
can't be - lieve so they don't and they won't ev - en try. With ev - 'ry bat - tle that's been

F♯/A♯
6fr
won, with ev - 'ry lit - tle thing I've
B
3
done, but I could - n't see it's not
C♯9sus4
4fr
clear to me.
C♯
4fr
All this
F♯
time. Oh, we've come a long,
C♯
4fr
long way. I've wait - ed a life
Badd9
- time for to - day. I'm pray - ing this mo -
C♯
4fr
- ment's here to stay.
A♭/E♭
All
E♭
this
A♭
4fr
time. We've come a long,

E♭
D♭add9
3fr
long way I've wait - ed a life - time for to - day. I'm pray - ing this mo -
E♭
A♭/E♭
E♭
A♭
4fr
- ment's here to stay. All this time. When ev - 'ry - one else
3
E♭
A♭/E♭
E♭
D♭add9
3fr
said I was wrong you gave me a rea - son to be strong. You gave me the will
E♭
A♭/E♭
E♭
A♭
4fr
to car - ry on. All this time.

Beautiful

Words & Music by Linda Perry

E♭7/D♭
4fr
Cm
3fr
B
wonderful, then suddenly it's hard to breathe.
-lirious, so consumed in all your doom.
E♭
6fr
E♭7/D♭
4fr
Cm
3fr
3
Now and then I get insecure from all the pain, I'm so a-
Trying hard to fill the emptiness, the pieces gone, left the puzzle
B
A♭
4fr
-shamed. I am beautiful, no
undone, is that the way it is? 'Cause you are beautiful, no
'Cause we are beautiful, no
Fm
E♭
6fr
E♭7/D♭
4fr
matter what they say. Words can't bring me down.
matter what they say. Words can't bring you down.
matter what they say. Yes words won't bring us down.

Cm
3fr
A♭
4fr
Fm
I am beau - ti - ful, in ev - 'ry sin - gle way. Yes,
You are beau - ti - ful, in ev - 'ry sin - gle way. Yes,
We are beau - ti - ful, in ev - 'ry sin - gle way. Yes,
E♭
6fr
E♭7/D♭
4fr
Cm
3fr
words can't bring me down. Oh, no.
words can't bring you down. Oh, no.
words can't bring us down. Oh, no.
Fm7
To Coda
1.
E♭
6fr
So don't you bring me down to - day.
E♭7/D♭
4fr
Cm
3fr
B

2.
E♭
6fr
E♭7/D♭
4fr
-day. No mat - ter what we do, no mat - ter what we say,
Cm
3fr
B
we're the song in - side the tune, full of beau - ti - ful mis - takes.
E♭
6fr
E♭7/D♭
4fr
And ev - 'ry - where we go, the sun will al - ways shine,
Cm
3fr
B
D.S. al Coda
but to - mor - row we might a - wake, on the oth - er side.

Coda
E♭
6fr
E♭7/D♭
4fr
- day.
Vocal ad lib.
Cm
3fr
B
Don't you bring me down
E♭
6fr
E♭7/D♭
4fr
Cm
3fr
to - day.
Vocal ad lib.
Free time
Bmaj7♭5
E♭
6fr
Don't you bring me down
to - day.

Born To Try

Words & Music by Delta Goodrem & Audius Mtawarira

A♭
E♭/G
Fm
B♭m
A♭
E♭/G
and pro - tect - ed from the walls of love. All that you see is me.
B♭m
A♭
E♭
E♭sus4
A♭
E♭/G
And all I tru - ly be - lieve that I was born to try, I've learned to love,
Fm
A♭
E♭/G
be un - der - stand - ing and be - lieve in life.
Fm
B♭m
A♭
E♭/G
But you got - ta make choi - ces, be wrong or right. Some - times you got -

B♭m
6fr
A♭
4fr
E♭
6fr
E♭sus4
6fr
A♭
4fr
A♭sus2
6fr
- ta sa - cri - fice the things you like.
But I was born to try.
1°
A♭
4fr
E♭/G
3fr
Fm
2. No point in talk - ing what should have been
A♭
4fr
E♭/G
3fr
Fm
A♭
4fr
E♭/G
3fr
and re-gret-ting the things that went on.
Life's full of mis-takes, des -
Fm
A♭
4fr
E♭/G
3fr
Fm
- ti - nies and fates.
Re-move the clouds, look at the big - ger pic - ture.

B♭m
A♭
4fr
E♭/G
3fr
All that you see is me,
and all I tru-ly be-lieve,
all that you see is me,
and all I tru-ly be-lieve
E♭
6fr
that I was born to try
I've learned to love,
Fm7
be un-der-stand-ing and be-lieve in life.
But you got-ta make choi-ces,
be wrong or right.

E♭/G
B♭m
A♭
E♭
Some - times you got - ta sa - cri- fice the things you like.
But I was born
to try
oh,
oh.
Fm7
No mat - ter who,
hey,
but you got - ta make choi - ces,
be wrong or right.
Some - times you got-
B♭m/A♭
D♭add9
Free time
N.C.
- ta sa - cri - fice the things you like,
but I was born to try.

Complicated

Words & Music by Avril Lavigne, Lauren Christy,
David Alspach & Graeme Edwards

Dm
B♭maj7
F
C
Uh huh, uh huh, that's the way it is.
F
Dm
1. Chill out, what cha yell - in' for? Lay back, it's all been done__ be - fore.
2. You come ov - er un - an - nounced, dressed up like you're some - thing else.
B♭add9
6fr
C
And if you could on - ly__ let it be__ you will see.______
Where you are ain't where_ it's__ at, you see__ you're mak - in' me______
F
Dm
I like you the way__ you are when we're driv - in' in__ your car
laugh out when you strike__ a pose. Take off all your prep - py clothes.
3° Lay back, it's all been done__ be - fore.

B♭add9
6fr
C
and you're talk - in' to me one on one but you be - come
You know you're not fool - in' a - ny - one when you be - come
And if you could on - ly let it be you will see
B♭add9
6fr
Dm
To Coda
some - bo - dy else 'round ev - 'ry - one else. You're watch - ing your back like you can't re - lax. You're
B♭add9
6fr
C5
3fr
try'n' to be cool. You look like a fool to me. Tell me,
D5
5fr
B♭5
F5
C5
3fr
why'd you have to go and make things so com - pli - cat - ed? See the way you're

D5
B♭5
F5
C5
5fr
3fr
act - ing like you're some - bo - dy else, gets me frus - trat - ed. Life's like this, you,
you fall and you crawl and you break and you take what you get and you turn it in - to
Gm9
B♭
hon - es - ty and prom - ise me I'm nev - er gon - na find you fake it, no, no,
1.
2.
F
no.
no, no, no,

Dm
B♭
no, no, no, no, no, no,
Csus4
3fr
C
F
D.S. al Coda
no, Chill out, what cha yell - in' for?
Coda
B♭add9
6fr
C5
3fr
N.C.
try'n' to be cool. You look like a fool to me. Tell me
D5
5fr
B♭5
F5
C5
3fr
why'd you have to go and make things so com - pli - cat - ed? See the way you're

D5
5fr
B♭5
F5
C5
3fr
act - ing like you're some - bo - dy else, gets me frus - trat - ed. Life's like this, you,
you fall and you crawl and you break and you take what you get and you turn it in - to
Gm9
1.
B♭
hon - es - ty and pro - mise me I'm nev - er gon - na find you fake it, no, no,
2.
it, no, no, no.

Don't Know Why

Words & Music by Jesse Harris

To Coda
Gm7
C7
F7sus4
B♭
B♭7
3fr
I don't know why I did - n't come, I don't know why I did - n't
come.
2. When I saw the break of day
B♭maj7
E♭maj7
D7
F11
I wished that I could fly a way,
'stead of kneel - ing in
the sand,
catch - ing tear - drops in my hand. My

Gm7
C7add13
F
F7
heart is drenched in wine.
Gm7
C7add13
But you'll be on my mind
F7
B♭/D
1.
F/C
2.
for ev - er.
- er.
B♭maj7
B♭7
E♭maj7
D7
Gm7
C7
Piano solo

Verse 3:
Out across the endless sea
I will die in ecstasy
But I'll be a bag of bones
Driving down the road alone.

My heart is drenched in wine etc.

Verse 4:
Something has to make you run
I don't know why I didn't come
I feel as empty as a drum
I don't know why I didn't come
I don't know why I didn't come
I don't know why I didn't come

For What It's Worth

Words & Music by Nina Persson & Peter Svensson

Fmaj7
Dm7
Am
G
Dm
1. Hey baby, come round, keep holding me down
2. Hey, please baby come back, there'll be no more lovin' attacks
3° Instrumental till *
F
and I'll be keeping you up tonight.
and I'll be keeping it cool tonight.
C
G
A four letter word
The four letter word

Dm
got stuck in my head, the dir - ti - est word that I've ev - er said.
is out of my head, come on a - round, get back in my bed.
F
C
It's mak - ing me feel al - right.
Keep mak - ing me feel al - right.
Fmaj7
Dm9
5fr
(1, 3.) For what it's worth I love
For what it's worth I like
*
Am
Fmaj7
you.
you.
And what is worse,
And what is worse,

Dm9
Am
To Coda
I real - ly do.
I real - ly do.
Fmaj7
Dm9
For what it's worth I'm gon - na
Things have been worse and we had
C
G
Fmaj7
run, run, run till the sweet - ness gets to you. And what is worse,
fun, fun, fun, till I said "I love you." And what is worse,
Dm9
1.
Am
I love you.
I real -

2.
Am
Fmaj7
-ly do.
For what it's worth
Dm7
Am
I love you.
Fmaj7
Dm7
Am
D.S. al Coda
And what is worse, I real - ly do.
Coda
Fmaj7
Dm9
5fr
Am
For what it's worth, I love you.
2° Vocal ad lib.

Fmaj7
Dm9
5fr
And what is worse, I real - ly do.
Am
Fmaj7
Ah, ah, ah. Ah, ah, ah, ah.
Dm9
5fr
C
G
Fmaj7
Dm9
5fr
rit.
Am7

The Closest Thing To Crazy

Words & Music by Mike Batt

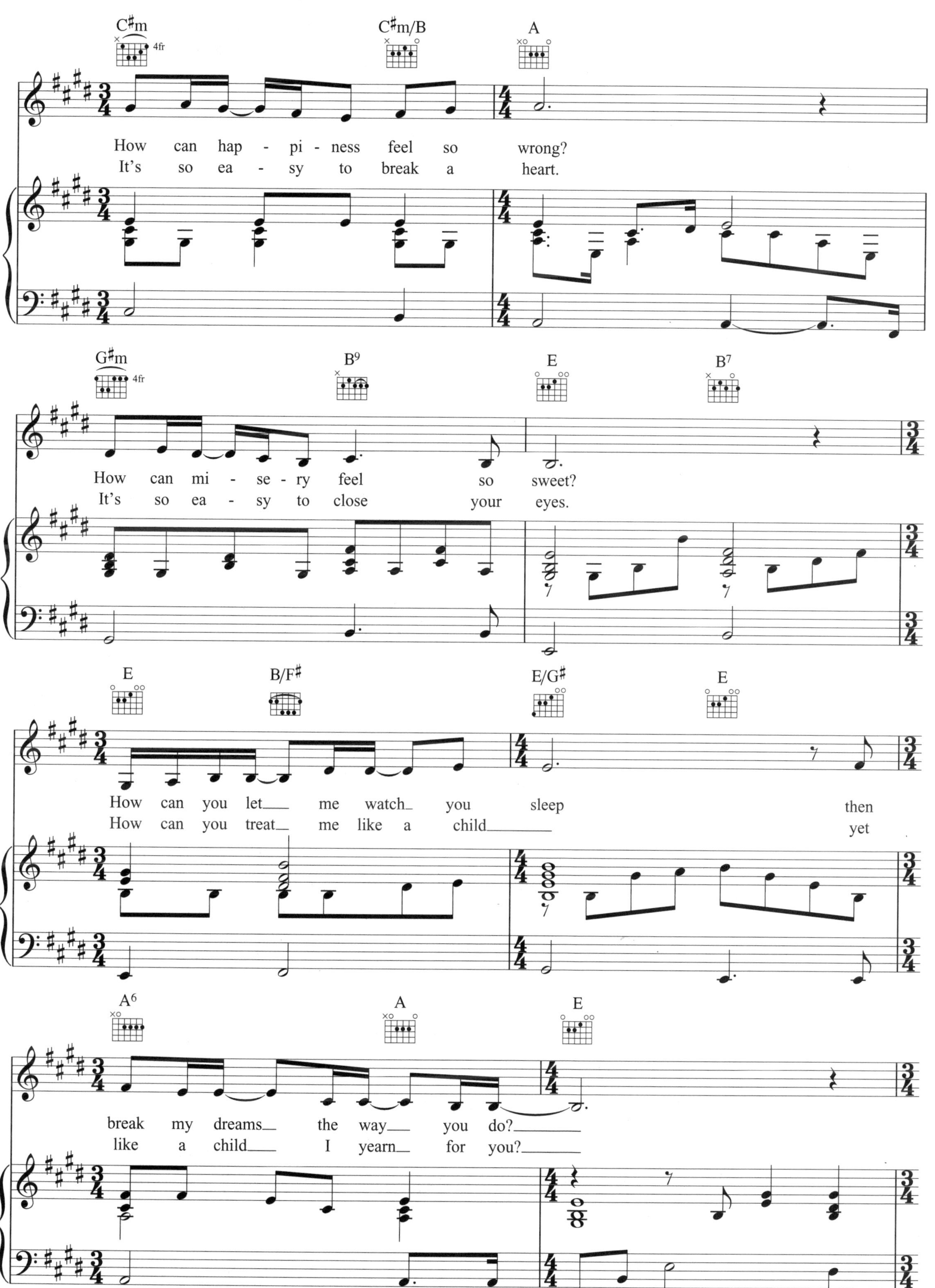
C♯m
4fr
C♯m/B
A
How can hap - pi - ness feel so wrong?
It's so ea - sy to break a heart.
G♯m
4fr
B9
E
B7
How can mi - se - ry feel so sweet?
It's so ea - sy to close your eyes.
E
B/F♯
E/G♯
E
How can you let me watch you sleep then
How can you treat me like a child yet
A6
A
E
break my dreams the way you do?
like a child I yearn for you?

C♯m
4fr
C♯m/B
A
How can I__ have got in so deep?
How can a - ny - one feel so wild?
G♯m
4fr
B9
E
B7
3
Why did I__ fall in love with you?
How can a - ny - one feel so blue?
This is the
E
C♯m9
clos - est thing_ to cra - zy I have ev - er been._ Feel - ing
F♯m6
B6
B
3
twen - ty two,_ act - ing sev - en - teen._ This is the

E
C♯m9
near - est thing_ to cra - zy I have ev - er known._ I was
F♯m7
Am(maj7)
nev - er cra - zy on my own___ and
E
C♯m
4fr
A
3
now I know_ that there's a link be - tween_ the two._
C
E
C♯m
4fr
Be - ing close_ to cra - zi - ness_ and

1.
B
E
B7/F#
be - ing close to you.
E/G#
Asus4
Am
E
2.
E
C#m
4fr
A
Bsus4
2fr
And be - ing close to
rit.
E
C#m7
4fr
Aadd9
Bsus4
2fr
E
you.
And be - ing close to you.
8vb

Heaven

Words & Music by Bryan Adams & Jim Vallance

Em7
Bm7
Cadd9
G/A
Aadd9
on - ly you and me, we were young and wild and free.
turn your world a - round, pick you up when you're feel - ing down.
Dadd9
2fr
Bm7
Aadd9
Now no - thing can take you a - way from me. We've been
Now no - thing can change what you mean to me. There's a
Em
Bm7
Cadd9
Gsus2
down that road be - fore, but that's ov - er now. You keep me
lot that I could say, but just hold me now. 'Cause our
Asus4
A
Aadd9
com - ing back for more.
love will light the way.

G
A
Bm
Dadd9
2fr
Gadd9
3fr
Ba - by you're all__ that I want when you're ly - ing here__ in my__ arms. I'm
Bm7
find - ing it hard__ to be - lieve, we're in hea - ven.
Love is all__ that I need and I've found it there__ in your heart. It
1.
Aadd9
To Coda
is - n't too hard__ to see___ we're in hea - ven.

2.
Aadd9
Em7
Gadd9
3fr
I've been wait - ing for so long for
Dadd9
2fr
Aadd9
some - thing to ar - rive, for love to come a - long.
Em7
Now our dreams are com - ing
Gadd9
3fr
Dadd9
2fr
true, through the good times and the bad. I'll be

Aadd9
A
D.S. al Coda
stand - ing there by you.
Coda
Aadd9
G
A
Bm7
Dadd9
2fr
Oh, oh, oh.
G
A
Bm
A
Oh, oh, oh.
We're in hea-
Con pedale
rit.
- ven.
8va

Hopelessly Devoted To You

Words & Music by John Farrar

Bm
E7
Amaj7
A6
eyes are not the first to cry.
I'm
Aadd9
F#7
Em/G
F#7
not the first to know there's just no get-ting ov - - er
Bm7
C#m
4fr
Bm
E
you.
2. I
A
C#m
4fr
D
know I'm just a fool who's will - ing to
head is say-ing "Fool, for - get him." My

Bm E7 Amaj7 A6
sit a - round and wait for you. But
heart is say - ing "Don't let go."
Aadd9 F♯7 Em/G F♯7
ba - by, can't you see there's no - thing else for me to
Hold on to the end, and that's what I in - tend to
Bm7 C♯m 4fr B E7
do.
do.
I'm hope - less - ly de - vot - ed to
Dm Dm/E A/F A/G A
N.C.
you. But now there's

Gm7
3fr
no - where to hide since you pushed my love a - side.
C
Caug
F
Fmaj7
I'm out of my head,
Adim7
D7♭9
4fr
Gm7
3fr
hope - less - ly de - vo - ted to you.
C7♭9
Hope - less - ly de - vo - ted to

Dm
Faug/C♯
F/C
you.
G/B
Gm7
3fr
1.
C
C7♭9
Hope - less - ly de - vo - ted to
Dm
Dm/E
Dm/F
Dm/G
A
you.
3. My
2.
C7♭9
B♭m
B♭m/C
B♭m/D♭
B♭m/E♭
F
- vot - ed to you.
Ooh.

How Come You Don't Call Me

Words & Music by Prince

D♭ G♭m/A G♭ A♭11

Spoken: But all wanna know baby is if what we had is good... Oh, oh, oh, oh.

D♭ G♭m/A G♭ A♭11 D♭ G♭m/A

Mm. Ah.

G♭ A♭11 D♭ G♭m/A G♭ A♭11

Yeah, ba - by. Uh, let me tell you something...

D♭
G♭m/A
G♭
A♭11
1. I keep your_ pic - ture be - side_ my_ bed._ Mm._
(Verse 2 see block lyric)
And I still re - mem - ber ev - 'ry - thing you said._
_ Mm._
Oh._
I al - ways thought our_ love_
_ was so_ right, I guess I was wrong._
Mm,_ mm.

D♭ G♭m/A G♭ A♭11 D♭ G♭m/A
Al-ways thought you'd be by my side, pa-pa, now you're gone. "And I'm
G♭ A♭11 G♭ D♭/F
not tryin' to hear that s**t." What I wan-na know ba-by, if what we had was good,
E♭m7 G♭/F G♭ G♭/G A♭11 N.C. D♭ G♭m/A
6fr 6fr 6fr 5fr
how come you don't call me a-ny-more?
1.
G♭ A♭11 D♭ G♭m/A G♭ A♭11
Vocal ad lib.

2.
G♭
A♭11
G♭
Am
Amdim
Some - times it feels like
I'm gon - na die.
B♭m7
E♭
3fr
If you don't call me, pa - pa,
ooh,
you got - ta try.
Won't get
E♭m7
6fr
G♭/F
6fr
G♭
6fr
G♭/G
5fr
A♭11
N.C.
down on my knees, won't beg you please,
please.
Oh,
oh.
Ooh,
G♭
6fr
A♭11
D♭
G♭m/A
G♭
A♭11
won't you call me some - time,
pa - pa?

Verse 2:
Still light the fire on the rainy night
Still like it better when you're holding me tight
Everybody said
Everybody said that we should never part
Tell me baby, baby, baby why
Why you wanna go and break my heart.

All I wanna know baby *etc.*

I Wish I Knew How It Would Feel To Be Free

Words by Billy Taylor & Dick Dallas. Music by Billy Taylor

B♭ D7/F♯ Gm B♭7 E♭ E♭/F B♭
wish I knew how it would feel to be free. I
B♭ E♭ B♭/D B♭ F C7
wish I could break all the chains hold - ing
F B♭ D7 Gm B♭7
me. I wish I could say all the things
E♭ E♭/F B♭ Edim B♭/F D7/F♯
that I should say, say 'em loud, say 'em

Gm
B♭/F
E♭/F
B♭
clear, for the whole round world to hear. I
B♭
D7
Gm
E♭
E♭/F
wish I could share all the love that's in my heart.
f
B♭
B♭
E♭
B♭
F
C7
Re - move all the bars that keep us a - part.
F7
B♭
D7
B♭
Gm7
I wish you could know what it means

E♭ E♭/F B♭ Em7(♭5) B♭/F D7/F♯ Gm7 Em7(♭5)
to be me, then you'd see and ag - ree that ev -'ry man
B♭/F E♭/F B♭ B♭ D7 Gm B♭7
should be free. I wish I could give all I'm
E♭ E♭/F B♭ E♭ B♭
long - in' to give. I wish I could live like I'm
F C7 F7 B♭ D7/F♯ Gm B♭7
long - ing to live. I wish I could do all the

E♭ E♭/F B♭ Edim B♭/F D7/F♯ Gm Em7(♭5)
things that I can do. Though I'm way ov - er - due I'd be
B♭/F E♭/F B♭ B♭ D7 Gm B♭7
start - in' a - new. Well I wish I could be like a
E♭ E♭/F B♭ B♭ E♭
bird in the sky. How sweet it would be
B♭ F C7 F7 B♭ D7
if I found I could fly. Oh I'd soar to the sun
8va

Gm B♭7 E♭ E♭/F B♭ Em7(♭5) B♭/F D/F♯
and look down at the sea. Then I'd sing 'cause I know
Gm Em7(♭5) B♭/F D/F♯ Gm Em7(♭5) B♭/F D/F♯
yeah, and I sing 'cause I know, yeah! And I'd sing 'cause I know,
Gm Em7(♭5) B♭/F D/F♯ Gm Em7(♭5)
I know how it feels, oh I know how it
Repeat ad lib. to fade
B♭/F D/F♯ Gm Em7(♭5) B♭/F D/F♯ Gm Em7(♭5)
feels to be free. Yeah I know how it feels, yes I

I'm Gonna Getcha Good!

Words & Music by Shania Twain & Robert John "Mutt" Lange

N.C.
want you for the week - end,
don't want you for a night.
I'm
on - ly in - ter - est - ed if I can have you for life,
yeah.
2. I
B♭5
B♭m
D♭
A♭
4fr
know I said I'm se - ri - ous,
and ba - by I am.
(Verse 3 see block lyric)
A♭/C
3fr
You're a fine piece of real es - tate, and I'm gon - na get me some land.

B♭m
D♭
4fr
Fm/A♭
4fr
G♭
Oh, yeah. So don't try to run,
Fm/A♭
4fr
G♭
D♭
4fr
ho - ney, love can be fun.
E♭m7
6fr
G♭
There's no need to be a - lone when you find that
G♭add9
G♭
N.C.
some - one. I'm gon - na get - cha while I got - cha in sight

I'm gon - na get - cha if it takes all night.
You can bet - cha by the time I say go, you'll nev - er say no.
To Coda
D♭
4fr
A♭
4fr
B♭m
I'm gon - na get - cha, it's a mat - ter of fact.
I'm gon - na get - cha, don - cha wor - ry 'bout that.
G♭
D♭
4fr
A♭
4fr
You can bet your bot - tom dol - lar in time, you're gon -

G♭
A♭
1.
B♭m
B♭m/A♭
4fr
-na be mine.
Just like I should, I'll get-cha good,
yeah.
D♭6
A♭
B♭m
B♭m/A♭
D♭6
A♭
2.
B♭m
A♭/B♭
B♭m
Uh, uh, uh, uh.
A♭/B♭
B♭m
A♭/B♭
Yeah, I'm gon-na get-cha ba-by.

B♭m
A♭
4fr
B♭m
I'm gon - na knock on wood.
I'm gon - na get - cha some -
A♭
4fr
B♭m
A♭
4fr
how hon - ey. Yeah, I'm gon - na make it good.
D.%. al Coda
A - yeah, yeah, yeah, yeah.
Oh yeah.
Coda
D♭
4fr
A♭
4fr
B♭m
I'm gon - na get - cha, it's a mat - ter of fact.
I'm gon - na get - cha, don - cha

Verse 3:
I've already planned it
Here's how it's gonna be
I'm gonna love you
And you're gonna fall in love with me, yeah.

So don't try to run. *etc.*

In These Shoes

Words & Music by Pete Glenister, Kirsty MacColl, William Correa & Melvin Lastio

Gm6
D7
Gm6
D7
let's make love on a moun - tain top, un - der the stars on a big
"Won't you walk up and down my spine, it makes me feel strang -
Gm6
D7aug
hard rock. I said "In these shoes?" "I don't
- ly a - live." I said "In these shoes?" "I doubt
Gm6
D7
Gm6
think so." I said "Hon - ey,
you'd survive." I said "Hon - ey,
D7
Gm6
N.C.
Gm6
To Coda
let's do it here." 2. So I'm
let's do it."

Gm6
D7
Gm6
D7
sit - ting at a bar in Gua - da - la - ha - ra, in walks a guy with a
Gm6
D7
far a - way look in his eyes. He said "I've got a
Gm6
D7
Gm6
D7
pow - er - ful horse out - side." "Climb on the back I'll take
Gm6
D7
you for a ride. I know a lit - tle place we can get there 'fore the break of day."

Gm6
D7aug
Gm6
I said "In these shoes?"
D7
Gm6
D7aug
"No way Jo - sé."
I said "Hon - ey,
Gm6
D7
Gm6
D7
let's stay right here."
Trumpet
Gm6
D7

Gm6
D7
Gm6
D7
Trumpet cont. sim.
Gm6
D7
Co-mo le gus - ta cam - i - nar.
Gm6
D7
Gm6
D7
No pue - de mon - tar a cab - a - lo.
Co - mo se pue - de bail - ar?
Gm6
D.%. al Coda
Es un es - can - do - lo.

Coda
Gm6
D7aug
Trumpet
D7
Let's stay right here.
Trumpet cont. sim.
Co - mo le gus - ta cam - i - nar.

Gm6
D7
Gm6
No pue - de mon - tar a cab - al - lo. Co - mo se pue - de bail -

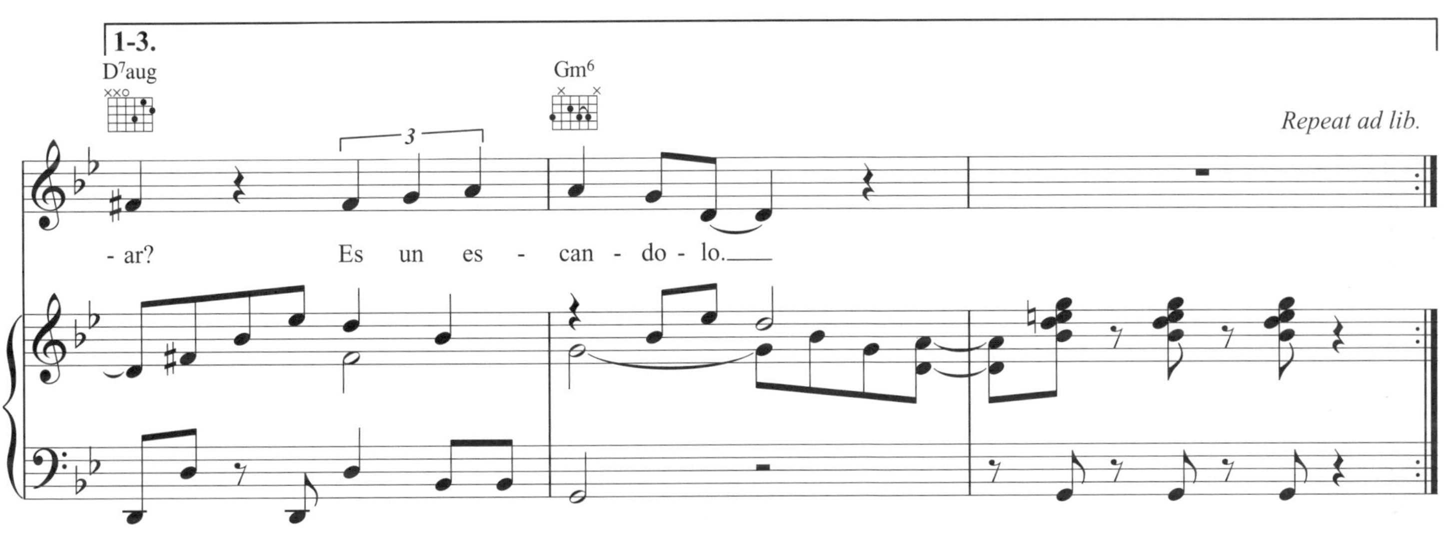
1-3.
D7aug
Gm6
Repeat ad lib.
- ar? Es un es - can - do - lo.

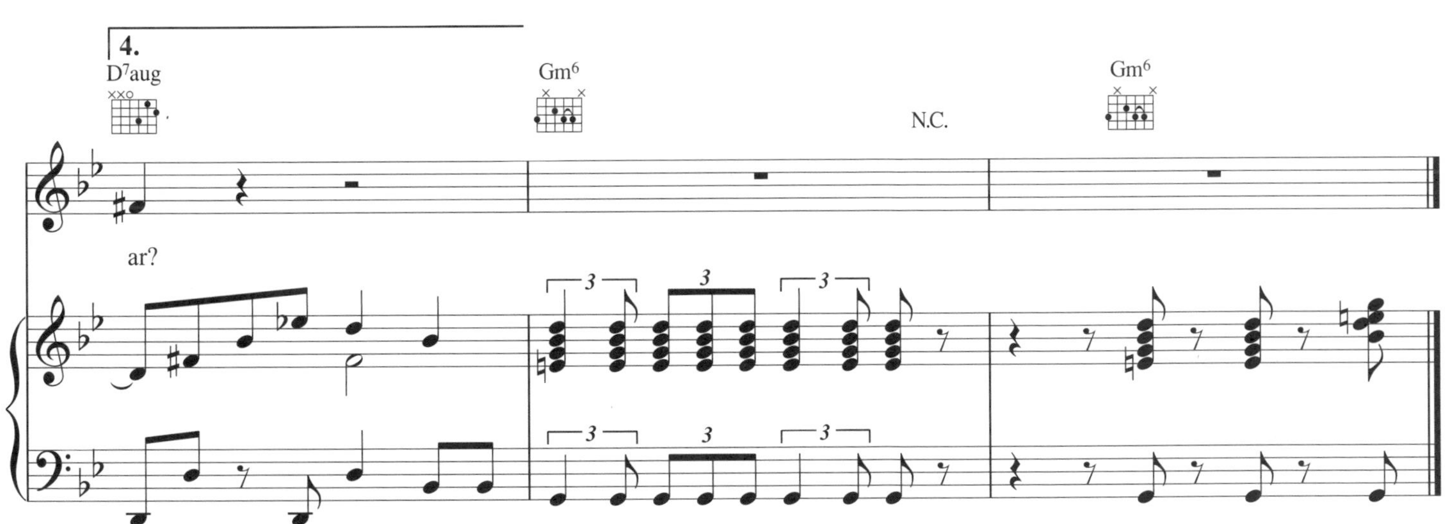
4.
D7aug
Gm6
N.C.
Gm6
ar?

Ironic

Words by Alanis Morissette.
Music by Alanis Morissette & Glen Ballard

G/B
C(add2)
To Coda
G/B
Am7
death row par - don two min-utes too late.
plane crashed down, he thought, "Well, is - n't this nice..."
meet-ing the man of my dreams, and then
Is - n't it i -
G/B
C(add2)
G/B
Am7
- ron - ic...
don't you think?
It's like rain
f
G
C
G
Am7
on your wed - ding day.
It's a free ride
G
C
G
Am7
when you're al - read - y paid.
It's the good ad - vice

G
C
G
Am7
that you just did - n't take.
Bb
F
1
G
Who would - 've thought... it fig - ures.
Mis - ter
mf
2
G
Fmaj7
Well, life has a fun - ny way of sneak-ing up on
mf
G6
Fmaj7
you when you think ev - 'ry-thing's O. K. and ev - 'ry-thing's go - ing right.

G6
Fmaj7
And life has a fun - ny way of help-ing you out
when you think ev-'ry-thing's gone wrong and ev-'ry-thing blows up in your face.
C
D.S. al Coda
A
CODA
G/B
Am7
meet-ing his beau - ti - ful wife.
mp
G/B
C(add2)
And is - n't it i - ron - ic... don't you

G/B
Am7
G/B
C(add2)
think? A lit - tle too i - ron - ic... and yeah, I
G/B
Am7
G
C
real - ly do think... it's like rain on your
f
G
Am7
G
C
wed - ding day. It's a free ride when you're
G
Am7
G
C
al - read - y paid. It's the good ad - vice that you

G
Am7
B♭
F
G
just did - n't take. _ And who would have thought, _ it fig-ures. ___
dim.
Fmaj7
G6
Fmaj7
___ And _ you know life has a fun-ny way of sneak-ing up on
mp
G6
Fmaj7
G6
you. ___ Life has a fun-ny, fun-ny way ___ of _ help - ing _ you out, _
Fmaj7
___ help - ing _ you out.

Love At First Sight

Words & Music by Kylie Minogue, Richard Stannard, Julian Gallagher, Ash Howes & Martin Harrington

𝄋
C♭add9
D♭
E♭m
Ev - 'ry - thing went from wrong to right, and the
stars came out and filled up the sky. The mu - sic you were play - ing real - ly
blew my mind. It was love at first sight. 'Cause
To Coda
C♭maj7
ba - by when I heard you for the first

D♭
E♭m
C♭maj7
D♭
E♭m
time, I knew we were meant to be as
1.
C♭maj7
D♭
E♭m
C♭maj7
one.
D♭
E♭m
D♭
E♭m
D♭
E♭m
2.
C♭maj7
D♭
E♭m
one.

C♭maj7
D♭
E♭m
Ba - by when I heard you for the first time, I knew we were meant to be as one.

D.%. al Coda
D♭
E♭m
C♭maj7
Coda
C♭add9
fr6
first sight. Love at first sight. Love
at first sight. Love,
ooh, it was first love at first sight. 'Cause

C♭maj7
D♭
E♭m
C♭maj7
ba - by when I heard you for the first
D♭
E♭m
C♭maj7
D♭
E♭m
time, I knew we were meant to be as
1.
C♭maj7
D♭
E♭m
one.
2.
C♭maj7
D♭
E♭m
one. It was love,

Verse 2:
Was tired of running out of luck
Thinking 'bout giving up, yeah
Didn't know what to do
Then there was you.

And everything went from wrong to right *etc.*

Murder On The Dancefloor

Words & Music by Gregg Alexander & Sophie Ellis-Bextor

G♯m7
4fr
know, I know, I know, I know, I know, I know,_ I know a - bout_ your
(Verse 2 see block lyric)
F♯m7
kind.___ And
G♯m7
4fr
so, and so,__ and so, and so, and so, and so,__ and so I'll have_ to
F♯m7
Emaj7
play.___

E
B
F♯m7
Amaj9
If you think you're get - ting a - way I will prove you wrong.
(𝄋) Don't think you'll get
I'll take you all the way boy, just come a - long.
Hear me when I say, hey... It's
G♯m7
4fr
Gm7
3fr
(On 𝄋 E)
mur - der on the dance - floor but you'd bet - ter not kill the groove.

F♯m7
Gm7
3fr
Hey, hey, hey. It's
G♯m7
4fr
Gm7
3fr
mur - der on the dance - floor
but you'd bet - ter not steal the moves
F♯m7
E5
To Coda
1.
D. J. Gon - na burn this god - damn house right down.
2. Oh I
2° turn this house a - round some - how.
2.
G♯m7
4fr
Gm7
3fr
Mur - der on the dance - floor, (on the dance - floor) but you'd bet - ter not kill the groove.

F♯m7
Gm7
3fr
Hey, hey, hey. It's
G♯m7
4fr
Gm7
3fr
mur - der on the dance - floor (On the dance - floor.) but you'd bet - ter not steal the moves.
F♯m7
E5
D. J. Gon - na burn this god - damn house right down.
G♯m7
4fr
Guitar

F♯m7
G♯m7
4fr
F♯m7
Emaj7
D.S. al Coda
Coda
F♯m7
Amaj9
G♯m7
4fr
burn this god - damn house right down. It's
mur - der on the dance - floor

Verse 2:
Oh, I know, I know, I know, I know, I know, I know, I know
There may be others
And so, and so, and so, and so, and so, and so, and so
You'll just have to pray.
If you think you're getting away
I will prove you wrong
I'll take you all the way
Stay another song, I'll blow you all away.

Hey, it's murder on the dancefloor *etc.*

My Heart Will Go On

(Love Theme From 'Titanic')

Words by Will Jennings. Music by James Horner

E
B
E
Bsus4
2fr
feel you. That is how I know you go
life - time, and nev - er let go till we're
Asus2
B
E
on.
gone.
Far a - cross the
Love was when I
Bsus4
2fr
Asus2
E/B
B
dis - tance and spa - ces be - tween us,
loved you, one true time, I hold you
E
Bsus4
2fr
Asus2
you have come to show you go on.
in my life, we'll al - ways go on.

C#m
4fr
B
Aadd9
B
Near, far, wher - ev - er you are, I be -
C#m
4fr
B
A
B
-lieve that the heart does go on.
C#m
4fr
B
Aadd9
B
Once more you op - en the door, and you're
C#m
4fr
G#m
4fr
A
E/B
B
here in my heart and my heart will go on and

1.
C♯m7
Bsus4
Aadd9
on.
Bsus4
B
2.
C♯m7
Bsus4
on.
Aadd9
Bsus4
C♯m7
Bsus4
A
C♯m/G♯
G♯7

Fm
E♭
D♭add9
You're here, there's no - thing I fear
E♭
Fm7
E♭
and I know that my heart will go
D♭add9
E♭
Fm
on. We'll
E♭
D♭add9
E♭
stay for - ev - er this way. You are

Fm7
Cm7
3fr
D♭add9
safe in my heart and my heart will go on
and on.
A♭/E♭
4fr
E♭
A♭
4fr
E♭/A♭
6fr
D♭/A♭
E♭/A♭
6fr
A♭
4fr
Mm.
Mm.
E♭/A♭
6fr
D♭add9/A♭
4fr
rit.
A♭add9
4fr
Mm.

Nothing Compares 2 U

Words & Music by Prince

F
C9sus4
F
C/E
Since U been gone I can do what - ev - er I want.
Dm7
F
C9sus4
F
I can see whom - ev - er I choose.
I can eat my din - ner in a fan - cy
C/E
Dm7
A7
res - tau - rant
but no - thing, I said no - thing, can take a - way these blues.
'Cause
E♭
B♭
E♭
3fr
B♭
C
no - thing com - pares, no - thing com - pares 2 U.

F
C/E
2. It's been so lone - ly with - out U here.
(Instrumental)
Dm7
F
C9sus4
Like a bird with - out a song.
(Ah.)
F
C/E
No - thing can stop these lone - ly tears from fall - ing.
Tell me,
2° F
2° C9sus4
Dm7
B♭
F
ba - by, where did I go wrong?
I could put my arms a - round ev - 'ry
(Verse 3 see block lyric)

C/E
Dm7
F
C9sus4
3
boy I see,
but they d on - ly re - mind me of U.
(Ah.)
F
C/E
I went to the doc - tor and guess what he told me, guess what he told me. He said
Dm7
A7
E♭
3fr
B♭
Girl U bet - ter try to have fun, don t mat - ter what U do. But he s a fool. Cause no - thing com - pares,
Dm
C
1.
no - thing com - pares 2 U.

Verse 3:
Instrumental
All the flowers that U planted Mama
In the back yard
All died when U went away
I know that living with U baby
Was sometimes hard
But I'm willing 2 give it another try.

Nothing compares, nothing compares 2 U *etc.*

Only Trust Your Heart

Words & Music by Sammy Cahn & Benny Carter

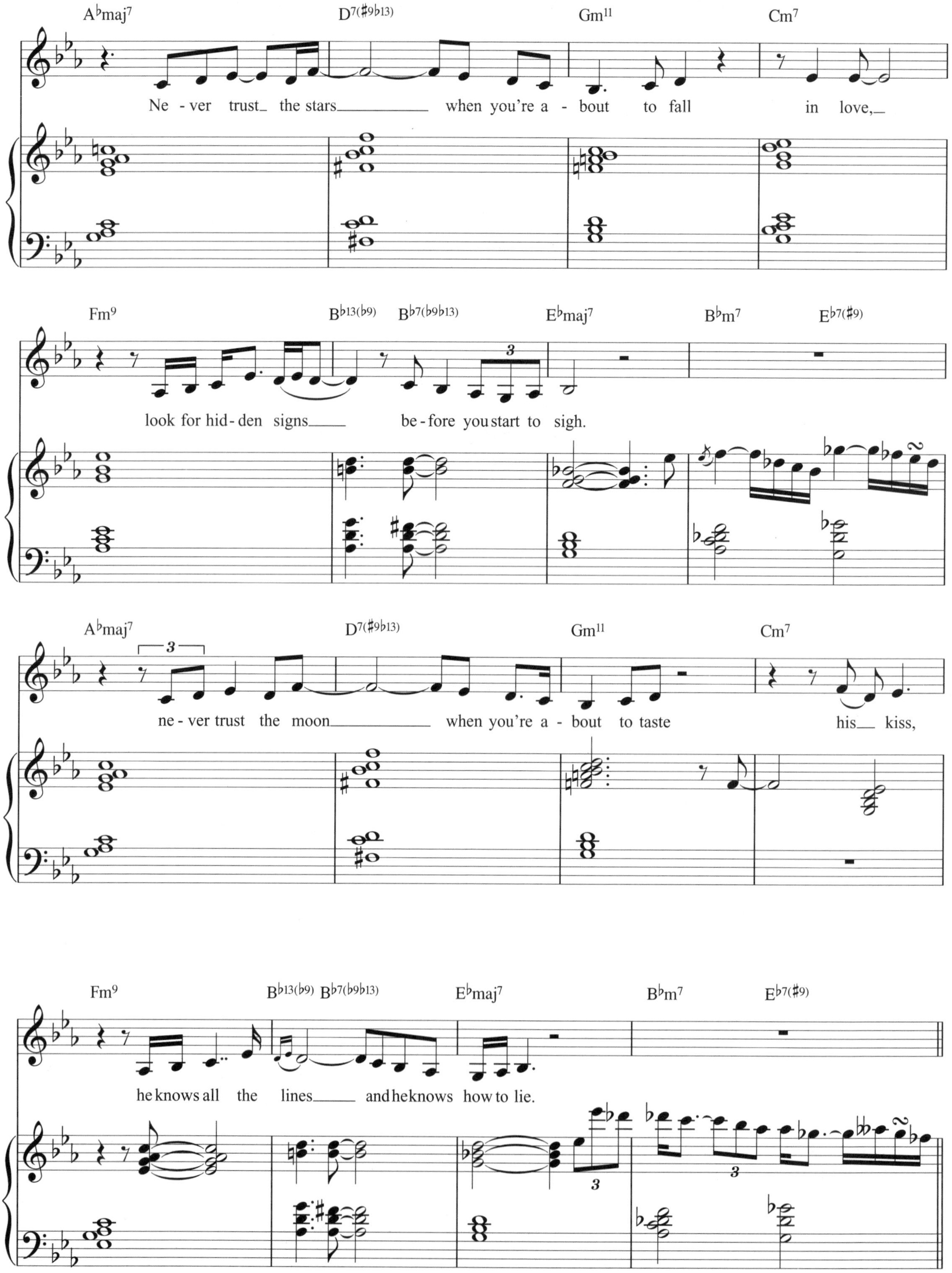
A♭maj7 D7(♯9♭13) Gm11 Cm7
Ne - ver trust the stars when you're a - bout to fall in love,
Fm9 B♭13(♭9) B♭7(♭9♭13) E♭maj7 B♭m7 E♭7(♯9)
look for hid- den signs be - fore you start to sigh.
A♭maj7 D7(♯9♭13) Gm11 Cm7
ne - ver trust the moon when you're a - bout to taste his kiss,
Fm9 B♭13(♭9) B♭7(♭9♭13) E♭maj7 B♭m7 E♭7(♯9)
he knows all the lines and he knows how to lie.

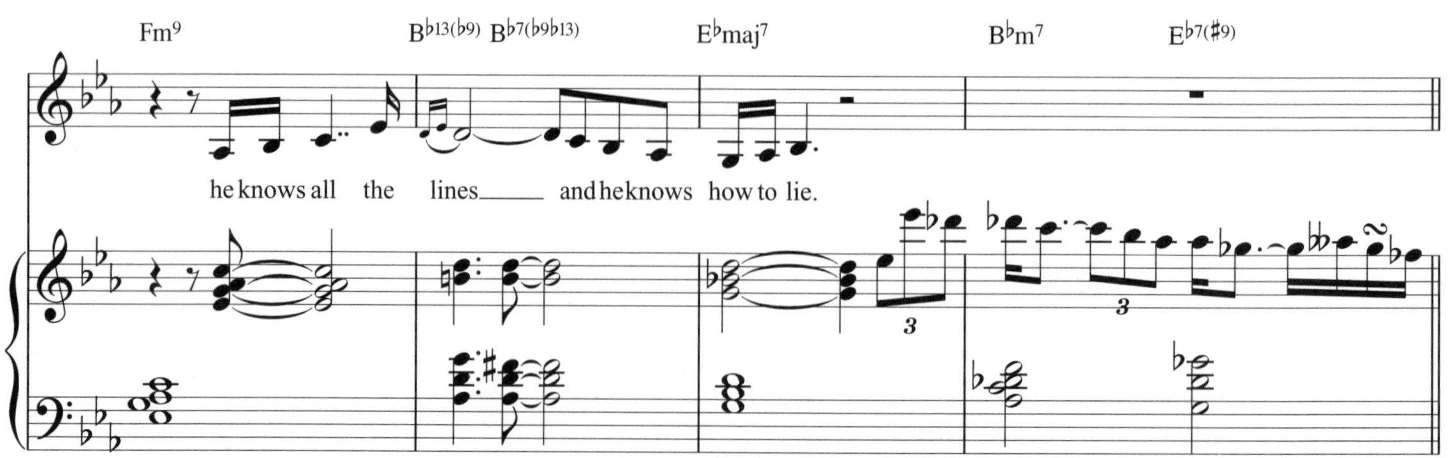

A♭maj7
C7(♯9)
Fm9
E♭m9
A♭13
Just wait for a night when the
Dm7(♭5)
G7(♭9)
Cm9
F13
B♭m7
E♭13
skies are all bare and then if you still care.
Am11(♭5)
D7(♯9♭13)
Gm9
Cm9
Ne-ver trust your dreams when you're a-bout to fall in love,
Fm11
B♭13
D♭13
C7(sus4)
C7
for your dreams may quick-ly fall a-part. So

Fm9
C♭maj7/D♭
E♭maj7
A♭13
Gm7
C7(♭13)
if you're smart
real - ly smart
Fm7
B♭13(♭9)
B♭7(♭13)
E♭maj7
A13
on - ly trust your heart.
A♭maj7
D7(♯9)
Gm9
3
3
Cm9
Fm9
B♭13(♭9)
B♭7(♭9♭13)

E♭maj7
swung ♪'s
B♭m7
E♭13
A♭maj7
D7(♯9♭13)
3
Gm9
Cm9
Fm9
3
B♭7(♯5♭9)
E♭maj7
B♭m7
E♭13

A♭maj7
C7(♯9)
Fm9
E♭m9
A♭13
Just wait for a night when
Dm7(♭5)
G7(♭9)
Cm9
F13
B♭m7
E♭13
the skies are all bare and then if you still care.
Am11(♭5)
D7(♯9♭13)
Gm9
Cm9
Ne - ver trust your dreams when you're a - bout to fall in love,
Fm11
B♭13
D♭13
C7
C7(sus4)
C7
for your dreams may quick - ly fall a - part so

Fm9
A♭m9
D♭13
E♭maj7
A♭13
Gm7
C7(♭13)
if you're smart,
real - - ly smart
Fm7
B♭13(♭9)
B♭7(♭13)
Am11(♭5)
D7(♯9♭13)
on - ly trust your heart
Gm9
Cm9
rall.
Fm11
On - ly
B♭13(♭9)
F♭maj7(♭5)
D/E♭
trust your heart.
8va

Son Of A Preacher Man

Words & Music by John Hurley & Ronnie Wilkins

B
cou-sin Bil-ly would take me walk-ing,
through the back yard we'd go walk-ing,
not 2°
then he'd look in-to my eyes,
Lord knows to my sur-prise. The
E
A
E
on-ly one who could ev-er reach me
was the son of a preach-er man. The
A
E
on-ly boy who could ev-er teach me
was the son of a preach-er man, yes he

B
A
was he was,
mm, yes he was.
1.
E
2.
D
How well I re - mem - ber
A
the look that was in his eyes,
steal-ing kiss-es from me on the sly,

B
B♭
B
E7
A
D
A
A
D
A
tak-ing time to make time, tell-ing me that he's all mine,
learn-ing from each oth-er's know-ing, look-ing to see how much we've known and the
on-ly one who could ev-er reach me was the son of a preach-er man. The
on-ly boy who could ev-er teach me was the son of a preach-er man, yes he

Verse 2:
Being good isn't always easy
No matter how hard I try.
When he started sweet talking to me,
He'd come and tell me everything is all right,
He'd kiss and tell me everything is all right,
Can't get away again tonight.

(Take A Little) Piece Of My Heart

Words & Music by Jerry Ragovoy & Bert Berns

Cm
fr3
B♭
D♭
) But with all the love I give you, it's nev-er e-nough. But I'm gon-na show you ba - by that a
B♭
B♭7
F/B♭
wo-man can be tough. So come on, come on, come on, come on in,
E♭
fr3
B♭
take a - no-ther lit - tle piece of my heart now ba - by.
E♭
fr3
B♭
Break it, break a - no-ther lit - tle bit of my heart now ho - ney.

Verse 2:
You're out on the street (looking good)
And you know deep down in your heart that ain't right
And oh, you never hear me when I cry at night
I tell myself that I can't stand the pain
But when you hold me in your arms I say it again.

So come on *etc.*

There Must Be An Angel (Playing With My Heart)

Words & Music by Annie Lennox & David A. Stewart

Dm7
G
this,
I'm thrown and ov - er - blown with
Instrumental
Am
G
F
bliss.
There must be an an - gel
G
Cm/E♭
Dm7
3
play - ing with my heart,
yeah.
C
Dm7
1. I walk in - to an emp - ty
room
2. And when I think that I'm a - lone

G
Am
G
and sud - den - ly my heart goes boom.
it seems there's more of us at home.
F
It's an or - ches - tra of an - gels
It's a mul - ti - tude of an - gels
To Coda
G
Cm/E♭
Dm7
and they're play - ing with my heart, yeah.
C
Fmaj7
Must be talk - ing to an an - gel,

A♭6
C
must be talk-ing to an an - gel,
must be talk-ing to an an - gel.
Fmaj7
A♭6
Must be talk-ing to an an - gel,
must be talk-ing to an an - gel,
C
Fmaj7
must be talk-ing to an an - gel.
Must be talk-ing to an an - gel,
A♭6
C
must be talk-ing to an an - gel,
must be talk-ing to an an - gel.

Am7
F
Must be talk - ing to an an - gel.
G7
Cm/E♭
Dm7
Must be talk - ing to an an - gel,
must be talk - ing to an an - gel.
1.
C
No-one on earth could feel like
2.
C
B♭
I must be hal - lu -
D7
Gm
3fr
- ci - na - ting, watch - ing an - gels ce - le - brat - ing.

B♭
D7
Gm
3fr
Could this be re - ac - ti - va - ting, all my sen - ses
B♭
D7
dis - lo - cat - ing. This must be a strange de - cep - tion,
Gm
3fr
C7
3fr
by ce - les - tial in - ter - ven - tion. leav - ing me the
F
G
D.S. al Coda
re - col - lec - tion of your heav - en - ly con - nec - tion.

Coda
C
Dm7
I walk in - to an emp - ty room,
G
Am
sud-den - ly my heart goes boom.
F
It's an orch - es - tra of an - - gels,
G
Cm/E♭
Dm7
they're play - ing with my heart. Yeah.

C
Dm7
Do da do da do da dun da, da
G
Am
G
da, da da.
F
G
Do da do da do da dun da, da da, da
Cm/E♭
Dm7
C
Repeat ad lib. to fade
Harmonica
da, yeah.

A Thousand Miles

Words & Music by Vanessa Carlton

E5
F♯
B/D♯
N.C.
E5
F♯
N.C.
B/D♯
E5
N.C.
Star - ing blank - ly a - head, just mak - ing my way,
E5
F♯
N.C.
B/D♯
E5
N.C.
E5
F♯
B/D♯
E5
just mak - ing a way through the crowd.
To Coda
F♯
B/D♯
E5
E
B/F♯
D♯m7
N.C.
E
B/F♯
D♯m7
N.C.
And I need you, and I miss you.
E
B/F♯
D♯m7
N.C.
E5
F♯
F♯/E
F♯
And now I won - der: if I could fall in -

D♯m F♯/E F♯ D♯m F♯/E
-to the sky, do you think time would pass me by? 'Cause
F♯ D♯m F♯/E G♯m7 F♯/A♯ F♯
4fr
you know I'd walk a thou - sand miles if I could just see you
1.
E5 F♯ B/D♯ E5 F♯ B/D♯ E5
to - night.
2. It's
2.
E5 F♯ B/D♯ E5 F♯ B/D♯ E5 F♯ B/D♯ E5

Emaj7 B/F# D#m E6 F#/G# F#/A# F#5/B F#5/C#
And I, I don't wan - na let you know.
F#/G# F#/A# F#5/B F#5/C# F#/G# F#/A#
I, I drown in your me - mo - ry. I, I
F#5/B F#5/C# F#/G# F#/A# F#sus4
D.S. al Coda
don't wan - na let this go. I, I don't.
Coda
E B/F# D#m7 N.C. E B/F# D#m7 N.C.
And I still need you, and I still miss you.

E
B/F#
D#m7
N.C.
E
F#
And now I won - der: if
F#/E
F#
D#m
F#/E
F#
I could fall in - to the sky, do you think time would
(2nd time ad lib. melody)
D#m
F#/E
F#
D#m
F#/E
pass us by? 'Cause you know I'd walk a thou - sand miles if I could
1.
G#m7
4fr
F#/A#
F#
just see you. If

Verse 2:
It's always times like these
When I think of you
And I wonder if you ever think of me.
'Cause everything's so wrong
And I don't belong
Living in your precious memory.
'Cause I need you
And I miss you
And now I wonder:

If I could fall into the sky *etc.*

Time After Time

Words & Music by Cyndi Lauper & Robert Hyman

Dm/C
C
Dm/C
C
Dm/C
C
Caught up in cir - cles, con - fu - sion is
You're call - ing to me, I can't hear what
watch - ing through wind - dows you're won - der - ing if
Dm/C
C
F
G
Em
F
G
no-thing new. Flash - back, warm nights, al - most left be - hind.
you've said. Then you say, "Go slow" I fall be - hind.
I'm O. K. Se - crets sto - len from deep in - side.
1.
Em
F
G
Em
F
G7sus4
Suit - case of me - mo - ries, time af - ter…

2, 3.
F G Em F G
The se - cond hand un - winds.
The drum beats out of time.
If you're lost you can look and you will
Am7 Fmaj9 G7sus4 C
find me, time af - ter time.
If you fall
G Am7 Fmaj9 G7sus4
I will catch you, I'll be wait - ing, time af - ter time.
C G Am7
If you're lost you can look and you will find me,
2° Instrumental till *

Fmaj9
G7sus4
C
G
time af - ter time.
If you fall I will catch you, I
Am7
Fmaj9
G7sus4
C
To Coda
will be wait - ing,
time af - ter time.
*
F
G
Em
Fmaj7
F
G
Em
Fmaj7
D.S. al Coda

Coda
F
G
Em
F
G
You say, "Go slow" I fall be - hind.
Em
F
G
Em
F
The se - cond hand un - winds. If you're lost
G
Am7
Fmaj9
G7sus4
you can look and you will find me, time af - ter time.
C
G
Am7
If you fall I will catch you, I'll be wait - ing,

Fmaj9
G7sus4
C
G
time af - ter time.
If you're lost you can look and you will
Am7
Fmaj9
G7sus4
C
find me,
time af - ter time.
If you fall
G
Am7
Fmaj9
G7sus4
I will catch you, I will be wait - ing,
time af - ter time.
C
Fmaj9
G7sus4
C
Repeat ad lib. to fade
Time af - ter time.

The Tide Is High (Get The Feeling)

Words & Music by John Holt, Howard Barrett, Tyrone Evans, Bill Padley & Jem Godfrey

Csus2
F
G
Csus2
3fr
not the things you do that tease and hurt me_ bad, but it's the way you do the things you
(Verse 2 see block lyrics)
F
G
Csus2
F
G
do to me. I'm___ not the kind of girl_ who gives up just___ like
C
F
G
C
F
G
that,___ oh no___ woh. The tide is_ high but I'm hold - ing on;
C
F
G
C
F
G
I'm gon - na be your_ num - ber one. The tide is_ high but I'm hold - ing on;

C
F
G
Dm7
G
3fr
5fr
I'm gon - na be your num - ber one.
Num - ber one.
My num - ber one.
1.
2.
A
Num - ber one.
(Whisper) Number one.
one.
D
Ev - 'ry time that I get the feel - ing,
you give me some - thing to be - lieve in.
Ev - 'ry time that I got you near me,
I know the way that I want it to be.

D
G
3fr
A
But you know I'm gon - na take my chance now, I'm gon - na make it hap - pen some - how.
D
G
3fr
A
And you know I can take the pres - sure; a mo - ment's pain for a life - time's plea - sure.
N.C.
3
3
Ev - 'ry girl wants you to be her man,
but I'll wait right here till it's my turn.
Dsus2
3
I'm not the kind of girl

Verse 2:
Every girl wants you to be her man
But I'll wait right here till it's my turn
I'm not the kind of girl who gives up just like that
Oh no.

The Time Is Now

Words & Music by Mark Brydon & Roisin Murphy

Am7
Dm
Am
Em7
Am7
Dm
I am emp - ty, so tell me you
Am
Em7
Am7
Dm
Am
care for me. You're the first thing
Em7
Am7
Dm
Am
Em7
Am7
Dm
and the last thing on my mind.
Am
Em7
Am7
F
1.
G
In your arms I feel sun - shine.

2.
G
Dm
Am/E
Em/G
F/A
Em/A
Dm
Give up your-self un - to the mo - ment.
Am
Em/G
F/A
Em/A
Dm
Am
The time is now.
Give up your-self un - to the mo-
Em/G
F/A
Em/A
F
Em/G
- ment.
Let's make this mo - ment last.
Dm
Am
Em7
Am7
Dm
Am
You may find your - self out on a limb for me.
(On 𝄋 see block lyric)

Em7
Am7
Dm
Am
Em7
Am7
Could you ac - cept it as
F
G
Dm
Am
part of your des - ti - ny?
I give
Em7
Am7
Dm
Am
Em7
Am
Dm
Am
all I have
but it's not e - nough.
And my
Em7
Am7
F
G
Dm
pa - tience are shot,
so I'm call - ing your bluff.

Am/E
Em/G
F/A
Em/A
Dm
Am
Give up your-self un-to the mo-ment.
The time is now.
Em/G
Fsus4
Em/A
Dm
Am
Em/G
F/A
Em/A
F
Give up your-self un-to the mo-ment.
To Coda
1.
Em/G
Dm
2.
Em/G
Gsus2
Let's make this mo-ment last.
mo-ment last.
Dmadd11/A
E7
E7/B
And we gave it time.
All eyes are

Am
Dm/A
Am
on the clock.
Time takes too much time,
Em
Am
Dm
Am
please make the wait - ing stop.
And the
Dm
Am
at - mos-phere is charged
and in you I trust.
[E]
[D]
F/C
G/B
D.%. al Coda
And I feel no fear as I
do as I must.

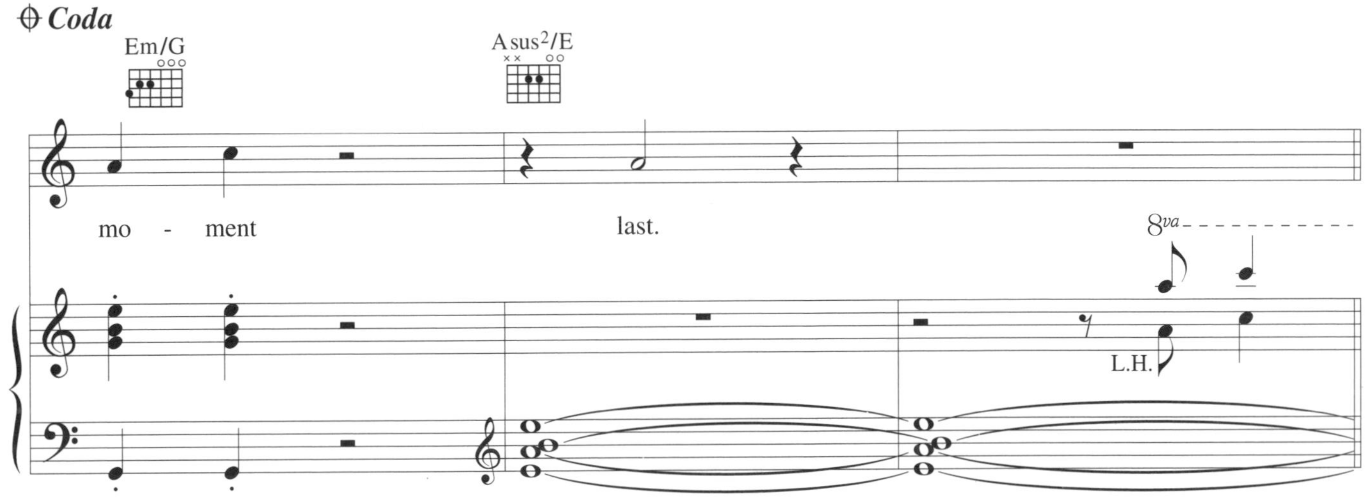

Repeat ad lib. to fade

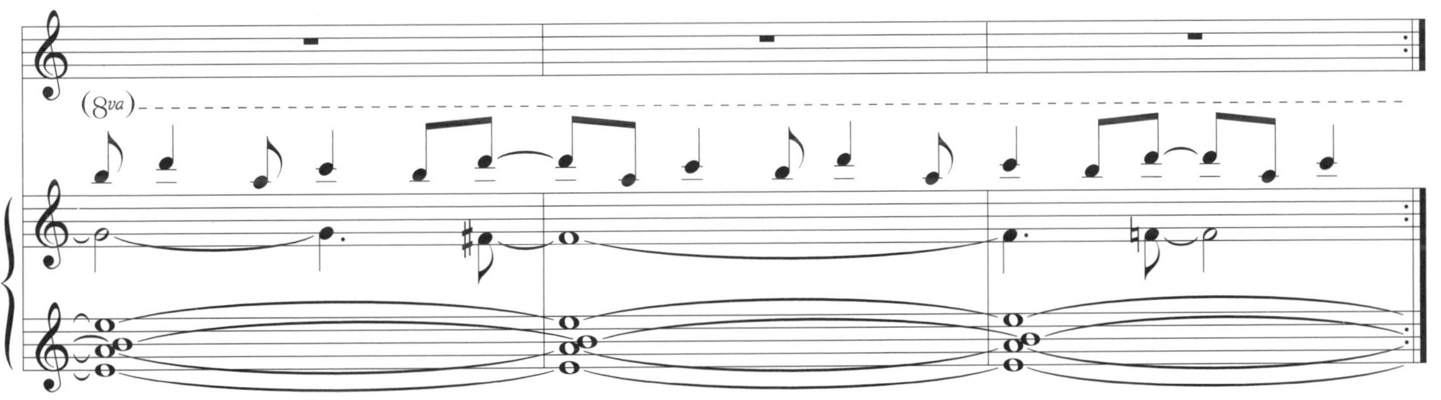

Verse 2:
On a promise
A daydream yet to come
Time is upon us
Oh, but the night is young
Flowers blossom
In the winter time
In your arms I feel sunshine.

Give up yourself unto the moment *etc.*

On 𝄋*:*
Tempted by fate
And I won't hesitate
The time is now
(Let's make this moment last)
The night is young
(The time is now)
(Let's make this moment last).

Give up yourself unto the moment *etc.*

Toxic

Words & Music by Cathy Dennis, Christian Karlsson,
Pontus Winnberg & Henrik Jonback

E♭
G
should wear a warn - ing.
It's dan - ge - rous,
I'm fall - ing.
Cm
Cm6
Cm
3fr
4fr
3fr
8va
2. There's no es - cape,
3. It's get - ting late
I can't wait.
I need a hit,
ba - by, give me it.
to give you up.
I took a sip
from my dev - il's cup.
E♭
G
Cm
3fr
You're dan - ger - ous,
I'm lov - ing it.
Slow - ly,
it's tak - ing ov - er me.

Cm6
4fr
Cm
3fr
Too high, can't come down.
Too high, can't come down.
8va
E♭
Los - ing my head, spin - ning round and round.
It's in the air and it's all a - round.
G
Cm
3fr
Cm6
4fr
Can you feel me now?
Can you feel me now?
8va
N.C.
Cm
3fr
With a taste of your lips I'm

E♭7
D7
D♭7
on a ride.
You're tox - ic
I'm slip - ping un - der
With the
Cm
E♭7
A♭
3fr
4fr
taste of a poi - son pa - ra - dise,
I'm ad - dic - ted to you.
Don't you
Gm7
D♭7
Cm
E♭7
know that you're tox - ic.
And I
8va
D7
D♭7
Cm
love what you do, but you know that you're tox - ic.

E♭7
1.
A♭
4fr
Gm7
3fr
D♭7
8va
2.
A♭
4fr
Gm7
3fr
N.C.
Don't you know that you're tox - ic.
Ah
8va
ah
ah.
Ah
ah
ah.

E♭7
D7
Taste of your lips I'm on a ride.
You're tox - ic
D♭7
Cm
3fr
E♭7
I'm slip - ping un - der.
With the taste of a poi - son pa - ra - dise, I'm ad -
A♭
4fr
Gm7
3fr
D♭7
Cm
3fr
-dic - ted to you. Don't you know that you're tox - ic.
With a taste of your lips I'm
8va
E♭7
D7
D♭7
on a ride.
You're tox - ic
I'm slip - ping un - der
With the

Cm
3fr
E♭7
A♭
4fr
taste of a poi - son pa - ra - dise, I'm ad - dic - ted to you. Don't you
Gm7
3fr
D♭7
Cm
3fr
E♭7
know that you're tox - ic.
In - tox - i - cate me now with your lov - ing now.
8va
D7
D♭7
Cm
3fr
I think I'm rea - dy now. (I think I'm rea - dy now.) In - tox - i - cate me now
E♭7
A♭
4fr
Cm6
4fr
with your lov - ing now. I think I'm rea - dy now.
8va

1/05 (53623)